© 2012, 2016 Age of Learning, Inc.
Published by Age of Learning, Inc., P.O. Box 10458, Glendale, California 91209.
No part of this work may be reproduced in whole or in part, or stored in a retrieval system,
or transmitted in any form or by any means, electronic, mechanical, photocopying,
recording, or otherwise, without written permission of the publisher.
ABCmouse.com and associated logos are trademarks and/or
registered trademarks of Age of Learning, Inc.

Library of Congress Cataloging-in-Publication Data
The Fox and the Stork/Age of Learning, Inc.
Summary: A fox plays a trick on a stork, but when the tables are turned
the fox learns a valuable lesson about how to treat others.

ISBN: 978-1-62116-003-8
Library of Congress Control Number: 2012912044

21 20 19 18 17 16 15 14 13 12   3 4 5
Printed in the U.S.A., on 10% recycled paper. ♻

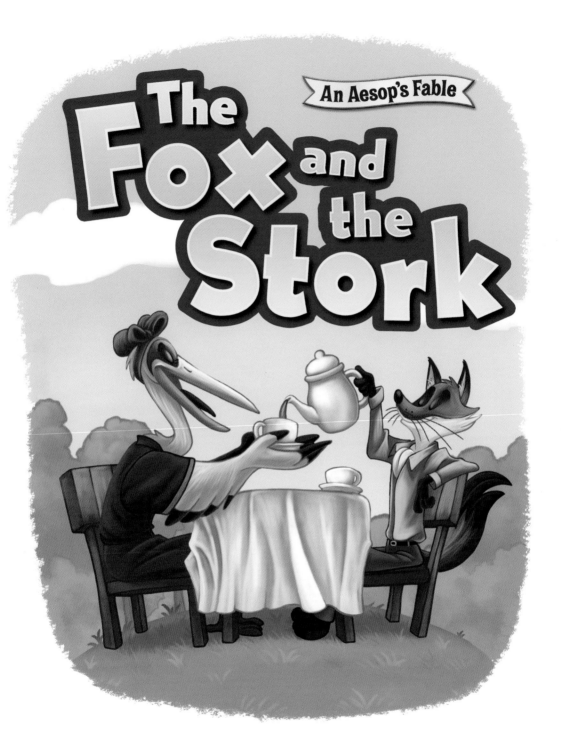

The Fox and the Stork

An Aesop's Fable

Age of Learning, Inc., Glendale, California
This book is also available at **ABCmouse.com**, the award-winning early learning online curriculum.

Aesop's Fables

What are Aesop's fables?
Legend tells us that Aesop lived a very long time ago in a place called Greece and became famous for telling stories that were intended to teach lessons about life. We call his stories Aesop's fables.

A fox invited his friend the stork to dinner.

Wanting to play a trick on his friend, the fox
served the stork a dinner of soup in a shallow dish.

The fox could easily lap up the soup with his
tongue. But because of her very long beak,
the stork could hardly drink a drop.

The stork left the dinner hungry and a little bit angry about being tricked.

The next day, the fox pretended to be concerned about the stork. He asked if she had liked his soup, since she had eaten almost none of it.

The stork said nothing bad about the soup, but instead decided to teach the fox a lesson. She invited the fox to join her for dinner at her house that night.

The fox arrived that evening and sat down, licking his lips hungrily while he waited for the stork to serve dinner.

The soup was served in tall, narrow jars. The stork could easily drink her soup with her long beak.

But the fox could not eat from his tall jar. He could only lap up the soup as it ran down its side.

The fox, of course, went home hungry that night, just like the stork had the night before.

The fox knew that he could not be angry with the stork, because she had simply done to him what he had done to her.

The fox learned an important lesson: You should always treat people the way you would like them to treat you.

The End

Moral of the Story

Treat others as you would like to be treated.

Glossary

arrive Definition: If you **arrive** at a place, you get there from somewhere else. **Example:** The fox **arrived** that evening and sat down, licking his lips hungrily while he waited for the stork to serve dinner.

concerned Definition: When people are **concerned** about something, they care about it and worry about it because they want it to be okay or do well. **Example:** The fox pretended to be **concerned** about the stork. He asked if she had liked his soup, since she had eaten almost none of it.

fable Definition: A **fable** is a short story that is intended to teach a lesson. **Example:** We call his stories Aesop's **fables**.

Greece Definition: **Greece** is a country in Europe that has many islands, mountains, and beaches. It has existed for thousands of years. **Example:** Legend tells us that Aesop lived a very long time ago in a place called **Greece**.

hardly Definition: When people can **hardly** do something, they almost can't do it at all. When people can **hardly** wait to do something, it means that they are so excited that they almost can't wait to do it. When there is **hardly** enough of something, that means there's almost not enough of it. **Example:** But because of her very long beak, the stork could **hardly** drink a drop.

intend Definition: When you **intend** to do something, you decide that's what you want to do. **Example:** Legend tells us that Aesop lived a very long time ago in a place called Greece and became famous for telling stories that were **intended** to teach lessons about life.

# Glossary

legend Definition: A **legend** is a story from long ago. **Legends** usually have events that could happen and other events that could not really happen. **Example: Legend** tells us that Aesop lived a very long time ago in a place called Greece.

lesson Definition: A **lesson** is something that a person is supposed to learn. **Example:** The fox learned an important **lesson**: You should always treat people the way you would like them to treat you.

moral Definition: The **moral** of a story is the lesson the reader is supposed to learn from the story. **Example: Moral** of the story: A mean trick will be repaid.

narrow Definition: When something is **narrow**, its sides are close together. **Example:** The soup was served in tall, **narrow** jars. The stork could easily drink her soup with her long beak.

shallow Definition: When something is **shallow**, it is not very deep. **Example:** The fox served the stork a dinner of soup in a **shallow** dish.

treat Definition: When you **treat** someone a certain way, you act a certain way or behave a certain way towards that person. **Example:** You should always **treat** people the way you would like them to **treat** you.

ABCmouse.com® Early Learning Academy

CHILD SAFE · NO ADVERTISING · NO POP-UP ADS · NO EXTERNAL LINKS ·

Online Preschool • Pre-k
Kindergarten • 1st Grade • 2nd Grade

More than 8,500 Fun-Filled Learning Activities!

Award-winning Curriculum with Proven Results

The leading and most comprehensive
online learning resource for children ages 2–8+.

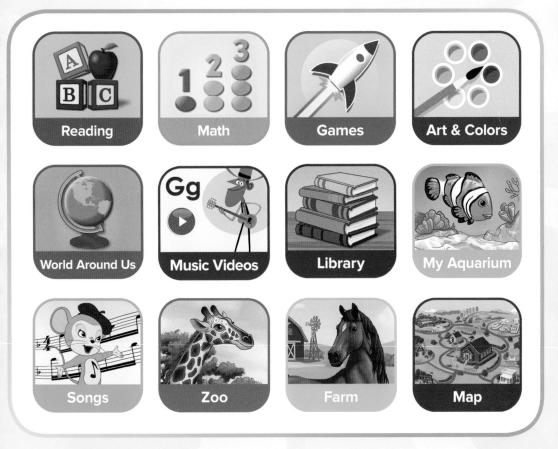

Reading | **Math** | **Games** | **Art & Colors**
World Around Us | **Music Videos** | **Library** | **My Aquarium**
Songs | **Zoo** | **Farm** | **Map**

Learn more at
www.ABCmouse.com

Short Vowels

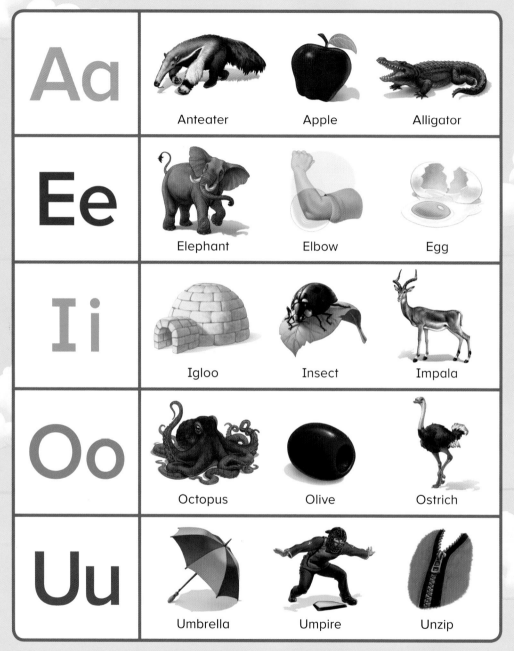

Aa	Anteater	Apple	Alligator
Ee	Elephant	Elbow	Egg
Ii	Igloo	Insect	Impala
Oo	Octopus	Olive	Ostrich
Uu	Umbrella	Umpire	Unzip

As you say the words for these items with your child, ask him or her to notice the first sound in each word. Explain that it is called the short (a, e, i, o, or u) sound.

Long Vowels

Aa	Apron	Acorn	April
Ee	Eagle	Easel	Eel
Ii	Ice Cream	Iron	Island
Oo	Ocean	Oval	Overalls
Uu	Unicorn	Unicycle	Ukulele

As you say the words for these items with your child, ask him or her to notice the first sound in each word. Explain that it is called the long (a, e, i, o, or u) sound.